Ho Ho Watanay

Birthe Kulich
Joe Berarducci
pictures by
fiona garrick

To the best of our knowledge, the material used in this
series is in public domain with the exception of the poem
"Sid Squid" (Book 3).

We would like to gratefully acknowledge the assistance we
have received from Susan Pond and Karen Epp in compiling
and testing the materials.

ISBN 1-895725-02-X (Book 2)
ISBN 1-895725-00-3 (Windsongs Recorder Method Series)

Contents

NAME: _____

Practice every day!

Date		M	Tu	W	Th	F	S
1							
2							
3							
4							
5							
6							
7							
8							
9							
10							
11							
12							
13							
14							
15							
16							

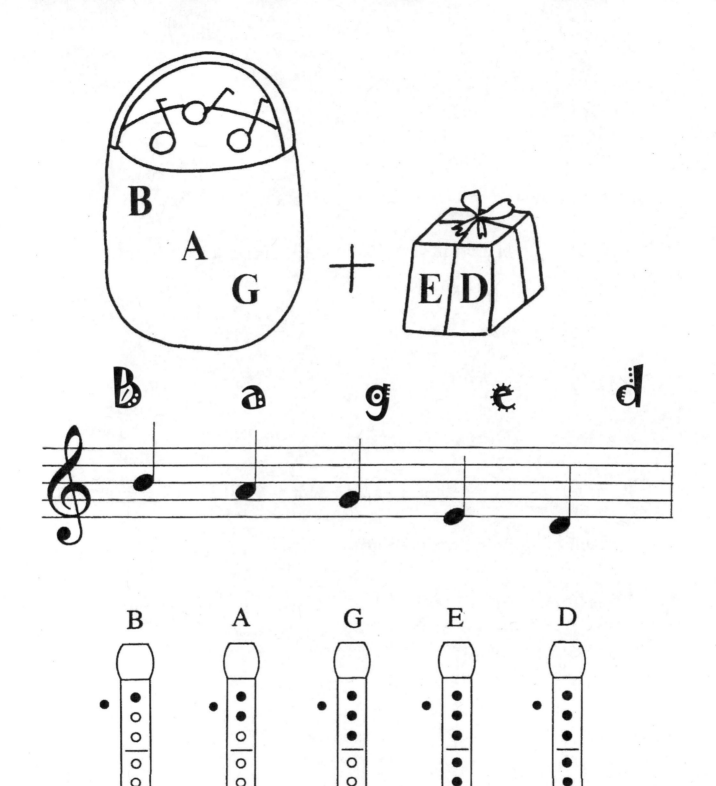

When we play or sing music, we have to hold notes for different lengths of time.

Each note or group of notes tells us to hold the sound for different amounts of time.

1. o - t aaaa says hold for 4 counts   G B WN

2. 𝅗𝅥 - t aa   says hold for 2 counts   tWO000

3. ♩ - ta   says hold for 1 count

4. ♫ - ti ti   says together we get 1 count.

How are each of these notes different to look at?

Write rhythm syllables under the following notes, then clap and say each pattern until you can do it without looking at the page.

1. ta _____   4/4

2. taa _____   2/4

3. ti ti _____

Can you clap and say all three?

PENCIL

7

Engine, Engine

Traditional

En - gine, en - gine num - ber nine. Go - ing down the

rail - road line. If the train jumps off the track,

will I get my mo - ney back?

≷ (Silent Ta)

Clap these tas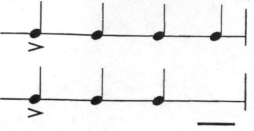

Repeat the pattern but drop the last one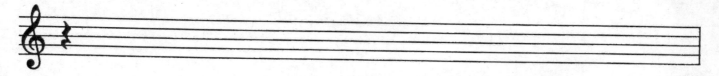

What sign can we use to show that we want silence for the 4th ta?

We use a **Rest** sign - a sign for a silent ta ≷

Practice writing some silent tas on the staff.

On the staff below write the rhythm pattern from the rhythm syllables under the staff. Use space 2, note A.

Remember the stems.

You can make up some patterns using silent tas, tas, ti tis, then share them. First write the rhythm syllables, then write the notes on the staff. Play the patterns on your recorder.

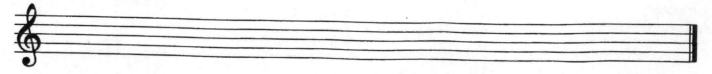

Rain Song

Traditional

Rain, rain go a - way. Come a - gain an - oth - er day.

Rain, rain go a - way. All the chil - dren want to play.

1. Sing the song and clap this ostinato pattern at the same time:

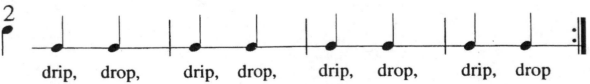

drip, drop, drip, drop, drip, drop, drip, drop

2. Invent other ostinato patterns to clap or play on a percussion instrument as you sing the song, e.g.

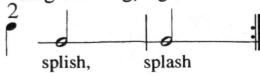

splish, splash

An <u>OSTINATO</u> is a repeated rhythm pattern.

10

The Pancake

Traditional verse
Melody B.K.

Mix a pan-cake, stir a pan-cake, pop it in the pan.

Fry the pan-cake, toss the pan-cake, catch it if you can!

Pease Porridge

Traditional

Pease por - ridge hot, pease por - ridge cold,
Some like it hot, some like it cold,

pease por - ridge in the pot nine days old.
some like it in the pot nine days old.

Old Mister Rabbit

American folk song

Old   Mis-ter   Rab - bit, you've got a might-y   hab - it of

jump-ing in my   gar - den and   eat - ing all my   cab - bage.

1. Circle the bar that has three different notes in it.

2. Circle the bar that has the note A in it.

3. Circle the bar which ends with a silent ta (rest).

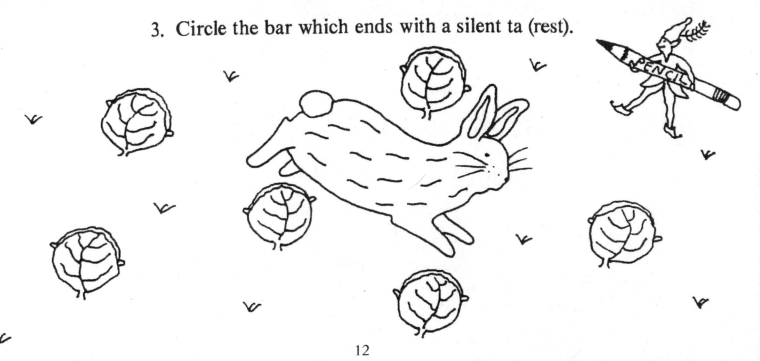

Nov 18th

Time Pattern

Bar line

2 bar line

Clap this row of tas.

$\frac{3}{4}$

7   7   7   7   7

Now we will make this row of tas into a pattern by making some HEAVY and some light. Listen while the teacher claps a pattern of heavy and light ta's.

Write an > sign under the heavy ones.

Can you hear and see the pattern? ____✓____

How many equal parts in each pattern? ____3____

Write this number at the beginning of the row of tas.

This number is the **TIME SIGNATURE.**

All songs have one.

Draw lines to divide the patterns.

These lines are called __Bar__ LINES.

The last one must be a __Doble__ __Bar__ LINE.

This shows **THE END** or __Redo__.

Look back at the songs in Book 1!

What are the TIME SIGNATURES? __$\frac{3}{4}$__ __$\frac{4}{4}$__

What is missing in the rhythm pattern below?

$\frac{3}{4}$

Did you find 2 things missing?

13

Fais Dodo

Louisiana French

Fais do - do, 'Co - las mon p'tit frè - re.

Fais do - do, ma - man est en bas.

14

The Dotted Half Note

We have learned about 3 different tas.

○ - t [aaaa]   - hold for 4 counts (beats)

♩ - t [aa]   - hold for 2 counts (beats)

♩ - t [a]   - hold for 1 count (beat)

To show a note that we ⟨hold⟩ for 3 counts we write

(♩) taa and a (·) dot

♩ + · = ♩.   t [aaa]   3-ee-el

So if ♩ is taa and

♩. is taaa

The dot adds____1____beat (count) to the note?

Practice writing ♩.(taaas) on the B line, A space and G line, on the staff below

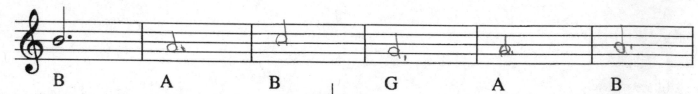

    B   A   B   G   A   B

In each rhythm pattern below add a ♩.(taaa) where there is a space and X. Write the rhythm syllables below. **Clap** and **say** each pattern while keeping a steady beat of ♩ ♩ ♩ **Play** the patterns on your recorder.

1.

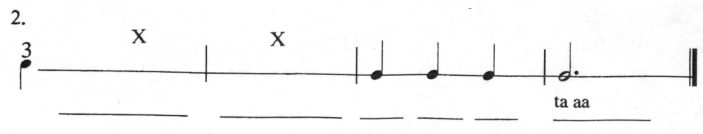

ta

2.

3

The Eagle

A

B.K./J.B.

1. King of the sky, soar - ing so high,
2. Cloud float - ing by, faint as a sigh,

lend me a feath - er so that I can fly.
not in - ter - rupt - ing the King of the sky.

The Flight

B

B.K./J.B.

Form: Play A part
Sing both verses
Play B part
Play A part once more

16

The Witch's Brew

1. Finish the witch's Rhythm Pattern

2. Brew a witch's song using the notes B A G and E

eye lash-es

se - cret ma - gic pow - der

dra - gon flies

toad - stools

liz-ards

Eye lash - es, toad stools, dra - gon flies, liz - ards ___ se - cret ma - gic pow - der.

Skin and Bones

American folk song

There was an old wo-man all skin and bones.

Oooo_____h!

2. She lived down by the old graveyard. Oooo_____h!
3. One night she thought she'd take a walk. Oooo_____h!
4. She walked down by the old graveyard. Oooo_____h!
5. She saw the bones a-layin' around. Oooo_____h!
6. She went to the closet to get a broom. Oooo_____h!
7. She opened the door and BOO!

Boo!

Ties

Clap and say the following pattern.

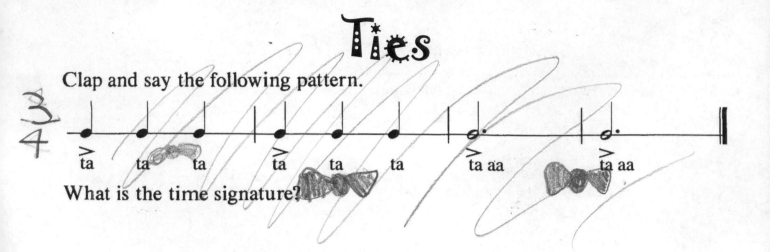

$\frac{3}{4}$

ta ta ta ta ta ta ta aa ta aa

What is the time signature?

We will repeat the pattern but join the last 2 taaas.

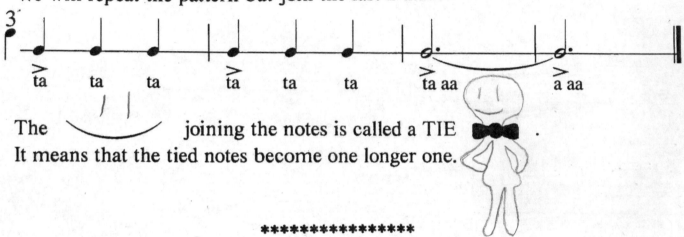

ta ta ta ta ta ta ta aa a aa

The _____ joining the notes is called a TIE .
It means that the tied notes become one longer one.

****

Clap and say the following pattern.

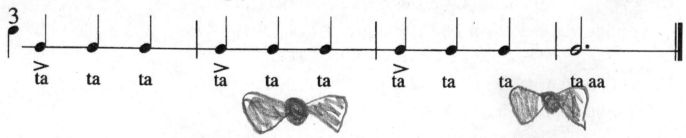

ta ta ta ta ta ta ta ta ta ta aa

Now we'll add some TIES!

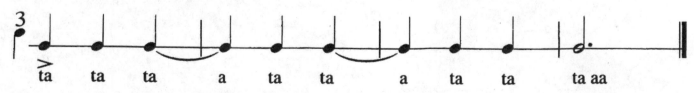

ta ta ta a ta ta a ta ta ta aa

Remember when you use a tie the second note loses its {t}
but still keeps its {a} !

and friends

When we want to show that there are 2 sounds on 1 beat we write

2 heads · · · 2 stems and | | 1 beam. ▬ They say ti ti.

When we want to show that there are 4 sounds on 1 beat we write

4 heads · · · · 4 stems and | | | | 2 beams. They say ti ka ti ka.

Many times in music we put ti and tika together

ti tika ' or tika ti

♪ = 1 beat (2 sounds)   ♬♬ = 1 beat (4 sounds)

♪♬ = 1 beat (3 sounds)   ♬♪ = 1 beat (3 sounds)

In the following rhythm patterns below 1 beat is blank. Add one of the tika patterns. You may use whichever one you like.

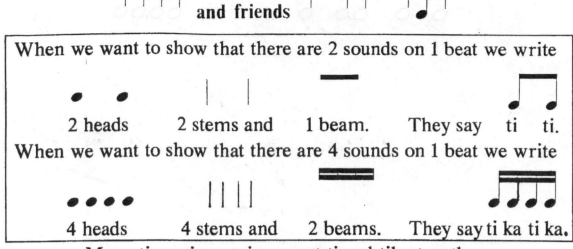

Can you: 1. Write the Time Signature; 2. Add a tika pattern; 3. Write the rhythm syllables below?

ta

Now can you 1. Clap and say the rhythm syllable while keeping a steady beat; 2. Repeat it, but from memory; 3. Play in on your recorder on any note?
Can you do all the same things for this second example? (reread the instructions if you forget).

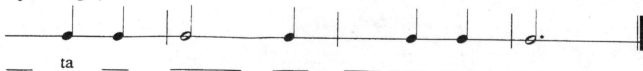

ta

Did you do all of the steps?

Old Man There

Folk tune

Old man there, sit-ting on a log, bid-ing his time, bid-ing his time.

Circle the tika tika pattern in "Old Man There".

Hop Old Squirrel

Afro-American folk song

Hop old squirrel, ei - dle dum, ei - dle-dum. Hop old squirrel,

ei - dle-dum dum. Hop old squirrel, ei - dle-dum, ei - dle-dum.

Hop old squirrel, ei - dle-dum dee.

Circle the tika ti (♪♪♪) patterns in "Hop Old Squirrel".

21

The Kite Song

D

J.B.

Win - dy day, win - dy day, oh what a sight!

I will fly my kite._____

Up so high look - ing at me.

Oops, it's in a tree._____

Which bars have this new note "D"?

Ho Ho Watanay

Iroquois lullaby

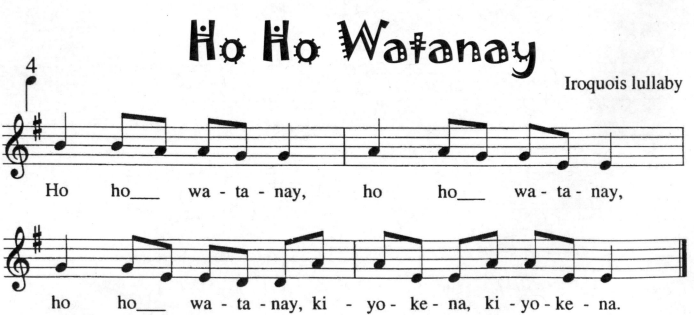

Ho ho___ wa - ta - nay, ho ho___ wa - ta - nay,

ho ho___ wa - ta - nay, ki - yo - ke - na, ki - yo - ke - na.

23

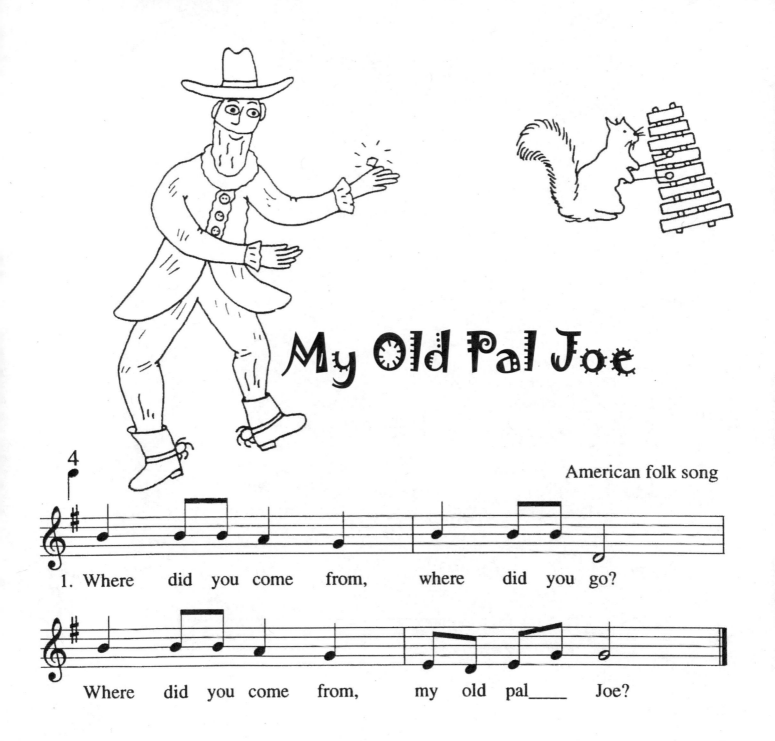

My Old Pal Joe

American folk song

1. Where did you come from, where did you go?

Where did you come from, my old pal___ Joe?

2 Come for to see you
Come for to sing
Come for to show you
My diamond ring.

24

Father is a Butcher

Melody B.K.

Fa - ther is a butch-er, and mo- ther cuts the meat, and

you're the lit - tle wie - ner who is run-ning down the street!

How many fingers do you lift when you skip from D to B?

Circle the D to B skips in the song!

Old Brass Wagon

2

ti ka ti ka

2

American singing game

Cir-cle to the left, old brass wa - gon. Cir-cle to the left,

old brass wa - gon. Cir-cle to the left, old brass wa - gon,

you're the one my dar - ling.

Prrrr
Prrrrr
Prrrrr

Ginger the Cat

Source unknown

3

Gin - ger the cat is on my knee.

Gin - ger has sil - - ky fur._____

Tick - le her chin and pre - sent - ly

you will hear Gin - ger purr._____

The Sandman

B.K./J.B.

Sand - man, take me a - way, take me a-

way to dream - land.

You can make a longer form by combining The Sandman and Fais Dodo (p. 14):

A part The Sandman

B part Fais Dodo

A part The Sandman

Take turns singing and playing the A B A piece.

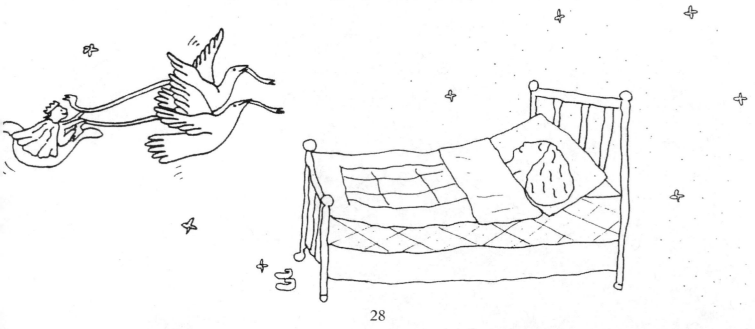

Kagome

Singing game from Japan

Ka - go - me, ka - go - me, ka - go - no na - ka - no

to - ri - wa, I - tsu I - tsu de - ya - ru?

Yo - a - ke no ba - n ni, Tsu - ru to Ka - me to

su - bet - ta, U - shi - ro no sho - men da - a - re?

29

Kagome

Japanese Singing Game

Translation: Kagome is a cage made out of wicker.
A bird is in the cage.
When will the bird escape?
One night near dawn.
* A crane and a turtle appear.
Who is right behind you?

* In Japan, the crane and the turtle are symbols of long life.

Game:

Form a circle holding hands. The bird "it" stands blindfolded (or covering eyes with hands) in the centre. All walk around in the circle while singing the song. At the end of the song, the person standing right behind "it" repeats (sings) the last two bars: "U-shi-ro no sho-men da-a-re? If "it" can guess who sings, "it" is free and can fly out of the cage. The game starts again with the new "it" (the person who sang the question) in the centre.

Note:

As the birds are set free they may form a group of recorder and/or percussion players.

As taught by
Professor Setsuzo Oka

Old Macdonald

American song

Old Mac Don-ald   had a farm,   ee - i - ee - i - o.   And

on that farm he   had some chicks,   ee - i - ee - i - o.   With a

chick chick here and a   chick chick there,   here a chick, there a chick,

every-where a chick, chick.   Old Mac Don - ald   had   a   farm,

ee - i - ee - i - o.

3 - 5 - 7 - 9 - 2 - 4 - 6 - 8

J.B.

3,   5,   7 'n 9,   swing your part-ner and keep in time.

Clap your hands. Stomp your feet.   Step to the right and   then re-peat.

Deux, quatre, six, huit,   tourne au-tour de ton par-ten-aire.

Frappe des mains. Tape des pieds. Vas à droite et   ré-pé-tez.

Far Below the Sea

Janet Greene

1., 2. I would like to be far be-low the sea

Fine

1. where the wa-ter's al-ways warm, where there is no rain or storm.
2. where the sea-weed gent-ly sway, where the shi-ny fish-es play.

D.C.al Fine

What kind of sounds would you hear far below the sea?
Find some instruments that might help you imitate those sounds.

Cruising

B.K.

How smoothly (legato) can you play the cruising song?

Congratulations!

You have now completed book 2.

Here is a game for you to test your musical memory. Below are a few bars of some of the songs in Book 2. Play these bars and then try to complete playing the songs by memory - without looking them up in the book.

Write the titles of
the songs here

1. _____

2. _____

3. _____

4. _____

.... and now on to Book 3